No. 1 December 1979

No. 2 April 1980

No. 3 July 1980

No. 4 October 1980

No. 5   March 1981

No. 6   July 1981

No. 7   December 1981

No. 8   May 1982

Viz Comic

THE BIG HARD ONE

FEATURING

LOTS OF BITS
OUT OF
ISSUES 1 TO 12

PLUS

Tommy 'Banana' Johnson
EXTENDED 10¼" VERSION

AND

Johnny Fartpants
DEBUT STRIP ~ FULL COLOUR REMIX

ORIGINAL CONTRIBUTING CO-EDITORS

CHRIS DONALD   JIM BIZ   SIMON DONALD

WITH CONTRIBUTIONS FROM

MARTIN STEVENS   ROGER RADIO
STEVE DONALD   GRAHAM DURY

**SPECIAL THANKS TO
TYNESIDE FREE PRESS
AND KARD BAR, NEWCASTLE**

This edition published in 1987 by Virgin Books, a division of
W.H. Allen & Co Plc, 44 Hill Street, London W1X 8LB

Copyright © by Viz Comic/Virgin Books

ISBN 0 86369 2362

Printed and bound in Great Britain

Reprinted 1987 (twice)

INTRODUCTION

When Viz Comic first appeared in December 1979 only 150 copies of issue 1 were printed. Five years later, by December 1984, the print run had gone up to 5,000. In fact, over the five year period a total of 26,600 copies were printed and sold. Enough, if they were laid end to end, to stretch all the way from London to Hampstead. Indeed, if the staples were then removed, and all the pages laid side to side, they would stretch from London to Buntingford (a small town near London).

It would have taken quite some time to remove those staples — over 53,000 of them in all. Even with the staples removed the total weight of all those comics would be in excess of 2148 pounds. That's 973 kilograms in metric measures. Certainly heavier than a small elephant.

Readers spent a total of £7,900 buying up those first twelve issues, all of which sold out. Over 790,000 pennies. In fact, over 1,137,600 pennies in pre-decimal currency. Enough money to buy a car, or a small house. Probably more old pennies than could fit into a post box.

And of course it took a lot of ink to print those 1,254,000 pages. Indeed, if it took a single teaspoonful of ink to print each page, that would be over 1,250,000 teaspoonfuls in all. Enough ink to fill a staggering 10,526 milk bottles.

Believe it or not, if you took those 26,600 comics, the 53,000 staples, a small elephant, 1,137,600 old pennies, a car, a small house, a post box, 1,254,000 teaspoons and 10,526 milk bottles and placed them all on top of each other, they would form a pile over 8 kilometres, or five miles high. Higher than the British Telecom tower.

"TOMMY'S BIRTHDAY" First Published July 1978 "THE DAILY PIE" ©1978 THE END

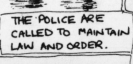

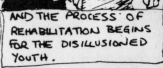

7

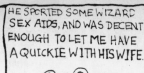

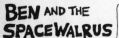
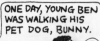

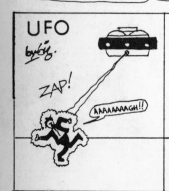

9

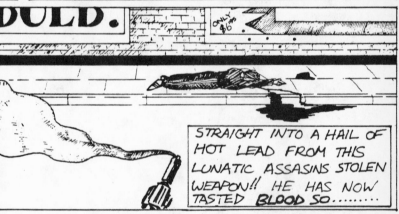

12

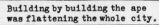

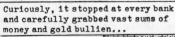

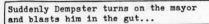

14

SKINHEED 3

THE PROBLEMS OF GROWING UP IN THE CONCRETE JUNGLE.

SKINHEED WAS TOLD HE WAS "FREE" AFTER SERVING 3 YEARS, SO HE WAS...

... HARD PRESSED TO UNDERSTAND WHY HE WAS NOT ALLOWED TO ENTER THE CITY'S NEW SHOPPING CENTRE WITH AIR CONDITIONING AND RECREATIONAL FACILITIES.

'KNOWN' TO THE POLICE AS AN OVER BOISTEROUS INDIVIDUAL, SKINHEED WAS ALWAYS BEING WATCHED AND SUSPECTED.

BITTER AND DISILLUSIONED WITH HIS SECOND CLASS STATUS IN SOCIETY, HE BLASTS A MOD WITH A ZIP GUN.

THE SOCIAL WORKERS PUT IT ALL DOWN TO HIS BACKGROUND, AND SOCIETY ITSELF. BEARING...

...THIS IN MIND, HIS RESPECT FOR SOCIETY, AND ALSO A PASSING WOMAN, IS LESSENED.

THE PROSPECT OF LONG TERM UNEMPLOYMENT LOOMS LARGE, AND AT THE EMPLOYMENT OFFICE HIS FRUSTRATION BECOMES APPARENT.

THE ASSISTANT WAS UNSYMPATHETIC AND NOT WHOLLY UNLIKE A COMPUTER. SKINHEED DID NOT LIKE HIM AT ALL.

IT WASN'T LONG 'TIL THE POLICE WERE CALLED TO PROTECT THE INTERESTS OF LAW ABIDING CITIZENS.

SKINHEED DOES NOT SEE THE ANSWER TO HIS ADOLESCENT PROBLEMS IN POLICE CUSTODY.

AS SKINHEED'S STRUGGLE FOR SOCIAL ACCEPTANCE GATHERS MOMENTUM, NEW MEASURES ARE CALLED FOR BY THE AUTHORITIES.

(CONTINUED IN NEXT ISSUE)

The man...

...A VIZ JOINT EFFORT © VIZ 1980

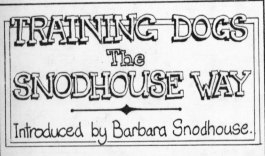

TED DEMPSTER AND THE "LOCH NESS MONSTER"

Locals at a small Scottish fishing village had for years been plagued by the infamous Loch Ness Monster who often emerged to eat sheep, scare babies and terrorise the folks.

The monster was in fact a giant rat.

He would frequently gate-crash the village local and bully the regular customers.

What's this piss Jimmy?

The simple village folk were powerless to stop the monster, so crack gumshoe Ted Dempster had to be summoned to the highlands to tackle this big legendary fiend, and end his reign of terror. Dempster is good at this sort of thing.

He would get drunk and vomit, leaving a trail of havoc after every visit.

URP!!

CD 29.6.80

One evening he arrived as usual...

Think I'll get pissed tonight

BAR

Dempster was in heavy disguise behind the bar...

Give us a whiskey, pronto

No dice. You're barred, mouse head

Nessie blew his top!

Get cancer, y'dog!

Grroar!!!

You're dead, y'bastard!

The locals waited anxiously outside ...

BAR

Eeee! Och! Oooh-er?

... and returned to find the monster slain. Dempster explained ...

It was simple. I left a bucket of water by the bar. Rats are very short sighted, so he drowned in it.

Yes indeed, Dempster has done it again. THE END

VINCENT GOES TO THE PICTURES
The tale of a lonely teenager rejected by his parents

ONE DAY VINCENT WAS GIVEN SOME MONEY TO GO TO SEE A FILM AT HIS LOCAL PICTURES. HE SET OFF...

COME BACK

NO

HI!

GET OFF THIS CARTOON, VIC.

INSIDE HE SAT DOWN WITH SOME POP-CORN AND COKE...

'ELLO 'ELLO

VINCENT'S STOMACH DID NOT AGREE WITH THESE "TRASH FOODS" AT ALL, AND HE HAD NO CHOICE BUT TO FETCH HIS LOAD IN THE CINEMA.

ALARMED

SPEECHLESS

WHAT THE?

THE DOC (J. Shiloe) VOMIT CARTOONS

---

professor piehead

THE PROFFESOR'S INDESTRUCTABLE CAR

OKAY JOE. READY TO TRY OUT MY NEW BULLET PROOF WINDSCREEN?

YIP!

TIM THE ASSISTANT

WINDSCREEN-OMETER

ANY DOCTORS IN THE HOUSE?

CD 14.6.80

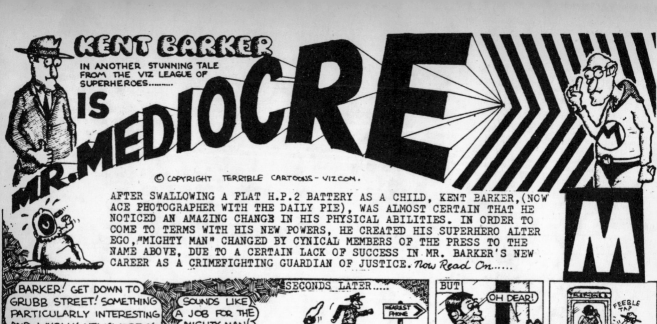

KENT BARKER

IN ANOTHER STUNNING TALE FROM THE VIZ LEAGUE OF SUPERHEROES.........

IS MR. MEDIOCRE

© COPYRIGHT TERRIBLE CARTOONS - VIZCOM.

AFTER SWALLOWING A FLAT H.P.2 BATTERY AS A CHILD, KENT BARKER, (NOW ACE PHOTOGRAPHER WITH THE DAILY PIE), WAS ALMOST CERTAIN THAT HE NOTICED AN AMAZING CHANGE IN HIS PHYSICAL ABILITIES. IN ORDER TO COME TO TERMS WITH HIS NEW POWERS, HE CREATED HIS SUPERHERO ALTER EGO, "MIGHTY MAN" CHANGED BY CYNICAL MEMBERS OF THE PRESS TO THE NAME ABOVE, DUE TO A CERTAIN LACK OF SUCCESS IN MR. BARKER'S NEW CAREER AS A CRIMEFIGHTING GUARDIAN OF JUSTICE. Now Read On......

BARKER! GET DOWN TO GRUBB STREET! SOMETHING PARTICULARLY INTERESTING AND WHOLLY NEWSWORTHY HAS OCCURRED!

SOUNDS LIKE A JOB FOR THE MIGHTY MAN!

YESSIR!

SECONDS LATER.....

IGNORING HIS VERY SERIOUS HEART CONDITION, BARKER RACES TO THE NEAREST PHONE TO CHANGE HIS IDENTITY TO THAT OF HIS INCREDIBLY POWERFUL ALTER EGO....

BUT OH DEAR!

OUR HERO GETS A BIT IMPATIENT

GENTS   LADIES

THA FULL!

PISS OFF.

OH......ER... RIGHT! FAIR ENOUGH! THANKS!

DISREGUARDING THE SHOOTING RHEUMATOID ARTHRITIS PAIN IN HIS FEEBLE SPINDLY LEGS, BARKER HEADS FOR A LOCAL PUBLIC CONVENIENCE TO EFFECT HIS TRANSFORMATION INTO "MIGHTY MAN". UNFORTUNATELY, AN EPEDEMIC OF DIARRHOEA PREVENTS THIS INCREDIBLE METAMORPHOSIS TO THE CAPED CUNT!

OH DEAR... I'M ALLERGIC TO CATS!

EAT SHIT MAC! THIS IS MY PAD!

PING!

SPYING A DUSTBIN IN A BACK ALLEY, AN IDEA HITS HIM RIGHT BETWEEN HIS SEVERELY MYOPIC EYES, AND HE DECIDES TO USE THE BIN AS A MAKESHIFT CHANGING FACILITY. BUT....

EVENTUALLY, AN OPEN MANHOLE PROVIDES THE TOOTHLESS, DOUBLY INCONTINENT, SEMI-SENILE WOULD-BE WONDER BEING WITH AN IMPROMPTU BATHROOM.

ACTION!

PAF!

HAVING MADE THE CHANGE, OUR MAN IS NOW READY TO APPLY HIS SKILL AS A SUPERHERO. HE FLIES OFF IN AN UPWARD DIRECTION, DESPITE THE FACT THAT HE CANNOT FLY. HIS OBVIOUS LACK OF X-RAY VISION AND MUSCLES OF STEEL, INDEED THE ABSENCE IN HIS MAKE-UP OF ANY SUPERHUMAN OR EVEN SLIGHTLY UNUSUAL POWERS OR TALENTS DOES NOT SEEM TO BOTHER HIM IN THE SLIGHTEST.

HAVING COMPLETELY FORGOTTEN HIS ORIGINAL INTENTIONS, MR MEDIOCRE WANDERS THE DARK STREETS, TRYING TO REMEMBER ANYTHING AND EVERYTHING.... THIS HAS BEEN YOUR INTRO TO THE MOST INEPT SUPERMAN IMITATOR IN THE WORLD. HE MAY APPEAR AGAIN... IF HIS HEART CAN STAND THE PACE.

SKINHEED 4

AS REGULAR READERS WILL RECALL, POOR SKINHEED'S SOCIAL PROBLEMS HAVE SNOWBALLED, AND THE S.P.G. HAVE NOW BECOME INVOLVED...

LUCKY I FOUND THIS CROWBAR IN MY LOCKER

CHARGE!

WHAT THEY LACK IN TACT AND SYMPATHY, THE S.P.G. TRY TO MAKE UP FOR IN ENTHUSIASM.

CRACK!

OWK!

← BRICK

ONCE AGAIN, SKINHEED WAS FORCED TO ADOPT VIOLENT MEASURES TO SURVIVE.

WAM!

HIS UNHAPPY BACKGROUND HAD BEEN A VIOLENT ONE, AND THE S.P.G. POSED NO IMMEDIATE THREAT TO HIS FREEDOM AND WELL BEING.

COME ON YOU BASTARDS!

AFTER SEVERAL MINUTES THE POLICE RETREATED, AND SKINHEED'S ATTEMPTS TO COMMUNICATE WITH THEM WERE IGNORED.

CHECK THIS OUT, MUSH!

WACK!

CD 9.6.80

AS THE POLICE SCOUR A NEARBY BUILDING SITE FOR BRICKS AND LEAD PIPES, SKINHEED K.O.'S A PASSER BY, AND THEN FLEES IN CONFUSION.

HE'S NOT IN 'ERE!

AS POLICE COMB THE AREA, SKINHEED GATHERS HIS SCRABBLED THOUGHTS AND YEARNS FOR A CHANCE TO BEGIN HIS LIFE AGAIN.

LOOK ANGRY, PLEASE

PISS OFF!

THE B.B.C.

BY NOW THE MEDIA ARE MORE THAN INTERESTED IN HIS STORY, AND THEY PURSUE HIM THROUGH THE STREETS FOR AN 'EXCLUSIVE'.

SOUNDS GOOD, NIGEL!

WANG!

AGAIN, A LACK OF UNDERSTANDING CAUSES FRUSTRATION, AND THIS IN TURN LEADS TO VIOLENCE.

WAAAAH!

HOOF!!

SKINHEED REVELS IN THIS PUBLIC ATTENTION, HAVING BEEN IGNORED THROUGHOUT HIS LONELY CHILDHOOD, AND IN GOES THE BOOT.

I THINK THE S.A.S. WOULD HELP DAVID

EVENTUALLY THE POLICE HAVE TO ADMIT DEFEAT, AND SUGGEST EXTREME MEASURES BE INTRODUCED....

YES MARK, JOLLY GOOD IDEA! WE'LL KILL THE BUGGER!!

...AND IN A WHITEHALL OFFICE A FINAL DRASTIC PLAN IS APPROVED.

(CONTINUED IN NEXT ISSUE)

OH NO! IT'S THE PATHETIC SHARKS

DARING DIVERS ROD SPLASH AND AQUA DRUMMOND WERE DIVING DEEP IN THE SEA!!

HEY!

WE GOT ONE!

THEY WERE ON A BIOLOGICAL MISSION TO INVESTIGATE PLANTS!

CD 4.7.80

SUDDENLY, AND WITHOUT WARNING, A PACK OF PATHETIC SHARKS, THEIR TAILS TOO LONG AND THEIR FACES IN THE WRONG PLACES, APPROACHED THE DIVERS.

THE DIVERS WERE PANIC STRICKEN.

HA HA! WHAT A FUCKIN' CRAP SHARK

HI!

BUT THE USELESS SHARKS WERE HUNGRY. VERY USELESS.

HAVE YOU GOT ANY CRISPS?

OR TOFFEES?

YO HO HO! CRISPS, TOFFEES! WHAT USELESS SHARKS!

THE AQUA TWOSOME DECIDED TO EXPLAIN TO THE SHARKS WHERE THEY WERE GOING WRONG...

YOU SHOULD EAT PEOPLE, NOT CRISPS!

OOH!

YOU SHOULD BE NASTY.

MMN... EAT PEOPLE, NOT CRISPS

...BUT THE MARINE BUFFOONS LEARN'T VERY QUICKLY.

SHREDD!!!!

RIPP!!

YIKES A BIGGUN!

..WAKE UP TUBBY! ♫ ♫ ♫

♫ DOOP-DI DOO! BOO-DOOP DI DOO! ♫ ♫

BZZT!

..TIME TO GET DRESSED..

...BUT WHO IS THIS STUCK IN THE JAM?!!

PLEASE DO NOT ADJUST
YOUR SET
H.M. GOVT. WARNING
RED ALERT
NUCLEAR ATTACK
YA GOT 3 MINUTES
SUCKAS...

AND DON'T FORGET TO BRUSH YOUR TEETH! ♫

"GOTTA BUZZ OFF 'N' GET BIZZY"
SEZ WALTER THE WASP...

...WATCH OUT FOR RAYS FROM SPACE!

YOU CAN'T MISS WITH

ARMITAGE SHANKS

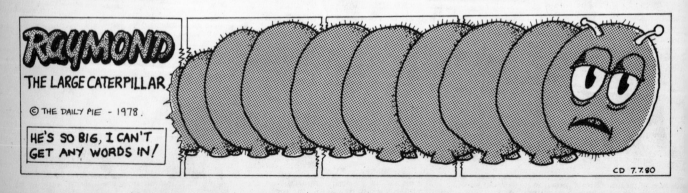

SKINHEED 5

CD 9.9.80

THE CONTINUING SOCIAL SAGA...

HAVING DEFEATED THE POLICE AND THE S.P.G. IN HIS STRUGGLE FOR FREEDOM, SKINHEED NOW WANDERS AIMLESSLY, IN SEARCH OF FREINDS.

FRUSTRATION AGAIN BUILDS INSIDE HIM, AND HE RELEASES IT ON THOSE WHO REJECT HIM.

A LACK OF UNDERSTANDING DEVELOPS BEETWEEN SKINHEED AND THE PEOPLE AROUND HIM...

IN A BLURRED STATE OF HUNGER AND CONFUSION HE LASHES OUT AT ANY OBSTACLE IN HIS PATH.

BUT EVEN AS HE EATS THE HEAD OF HIS LATEST VICTIM, THE S.A.S. HAVE ARRIVED AND ARE READY TO POUNCE.

AS HE PACES A GRIM SIDEWALK THE FIRST UNIT GO INTO ACTION...

... BUT DESPITE THEIR COURAGE, BRAVERY, EXTENSIVE TRAINING, SPLIT SECOND TIMING AND THE ELEMENT OF SURPRISE, SKINHEED WINS THE FIRST ENCOUNTER.

SKINHEED FINDS A WEAPON...

... AND USES IT AS BEST HE CAN TO DEFEND HIMSELF FROM HIS ATTACKERS.

BUT AS HE TAKES A WELL EARNED BREATHER IN HIS STRUGGLE FOR HAPPINESS, A HAND GRENADE IS SLIPPED DOWN HIS BACK!

AND SUDDENLY THE BATTLE IS LOST AMIDST THE HEAT OF A HUGE EXPLOSION !!!

AND SO SKINHEED IS BURIED AND FORGOTTEN. OR IS HE? WHO IS THIS EVIL FIGURE LURKING IN THE GRAVEYARD? CONTINUED IN NEXT ISSUE.

SWANT

SPECIAL WEAPONS AND NO TACTICS

DIVISION

LET'S ROLL!!

MERLiN

& THE DRAGON

25

Butch Cigarettes for men with really big cocks

A WILD JUNGLE AROMA

H M GOVT'S HEALTH WARNING:
ALWAYS CROSS ROADS CAREFULLY

OH NO! IT'S THEM BLOODY **PATHETIC SHARKS** AGAIN!

AHOY THERE

URP!

ONE DAY A GALLEON FULL OF SWASHBUCKLING PIRATES WERE LOOKING FOR DUBLOONS A'PLENTY.

AYE, AYE, AYE, AYE, I'M HUNGRY

YO HO HO, SHIPMATE

PRESS DARLING

I'LL CATCH US A BIG FISH ME'HEARTIES

BAIT

MEANWHILE, DOWN IN THE SEA, AN UGLY SWARM OF PATHETIC SHARKS WERE BUILDING SANDCASTLES...

IT'S A FISH

IS IT?

... WHEN THEY NOTICED THE PIRATES' BAIT.

EXCUSE ME, HAVE YOU LOST THIS FISH SIR?

SHIVER ME TIMBERS, A SHARK!

THE SHIT THICK SHARKS DECIDED TO RETURN IT TO IT'S OWNER.

GO AWAY Y'SHARK BASTARD!

YEAH! PISS OFF

AHOY THERE SHIPMATES, CAN'T YOU SEE THAT THIS IS A CRAP SHARK

WHAT ARE YOU DOING? IS IT A GAME? CAN I PLAY?

AT FIRST THE PLUNDERING CUT-THROATS WERE TERRIFIED, UNTIL THEY REALISED THE SHARKS WERE CRAP.

IS THAT LEMONADE YOU'RE DRINKING! I LOVE LEMONADE

BLOODY HELL HOW CRAP!

ALL WAS WELL UNTIL THE HOPELESS SHARK FOUND THE SHIP'S CANNON.

YO HO HO AND A FLAGGON OF RUM! HE'S GOT THE CANNON!

JESUS

HEY LOOK! AN OLD FASHIONED CAMERA. SMILE EVERYBODY!

Hisss!

CHEESE

THE END

OOH! WHAT A POWERFUL CAMERA

BAM!!

CD 6.1.81

MR NUGGIN

MMMM....

MR NUGGIN ALWAYS WALKED TO WORK BACKWARDS ON MONDAY MORNINGS.

HE WAS USUALLY LATE, BUT ON THIS OCCASION HE COULDN'T FIND HIS OFFICE

ERM?

TWENTY REGAL, MATE

ERM! YES... TWENTY

HE FOUND A NEWSAGENTS AND SO HE DECIDED TO WORK THERE FOR THE DAY

AH! HMM... TWENTY. THAT'S 20p

SURE

E WASN'T TOO GOOD FOR BUSINESS

PISS OFF JOHN!!

Hi!

MR NUGGIN WAS QUITE HAPPY, BUT THE SHOPKEEPER WASN'T.

CD 21.1.81

... AND MR NUGGIN WAS SOON BACK ON THE STREET.

QUICK TEMPERED CHAP, THAT ONE!

HMM... BEDTIME!

HE THOUGHT IT MUST BE BEDTIME BY NOW, SO HE DECIDED TO FIND SOMEWHERE TO GO TO SLEEP.

ZZZZZ.... ...ZZZZZZ

VIZ

E FOUND A NICE PLACE TO SLEEP AND DOZED OFF...

BRRRM!!

WHEN HE WOKE UP HE WAS IN THE COUNTRYSIDE.

WAP!

NOW THEN, WHERE CAN ONE BUY A NICE HAM SANDWICH?

'DINNER TIME', HE THOUGHT.

END

SKINHEED 6

THE CONTINUING STORY OF ONE LAD'S STRUGGLE TO OVERCOME HIS SOCIAL PROBLEMS

FLASHBACK: IN THE LAST ISSUE SKINHEED WAS BLOWN TO BITS BY THE S.A.S. IN AN AMBUSH...

GET DOWN, GET DOWN, GET DOWN!

... BOOM!! THEN HE WAS COLLECTED AND BURIED.

BUT LATER THAT EVENING FRED FRANKENSTONE, A FRUSTRATED MALE NURSE, REMOVED THE BODY FROM THE GRAVE

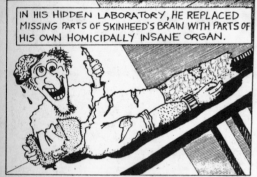

IN HIS HIDDEN LABORATORY, HE REPLACED MISSING PARTS OF SKINHEED'S BRAIN WITH PARTS OF HIS OWN HOMICIDALLY INSANE ORGAN.

ZAP!

FRANKENSTONE THEN USED 10 MILLION VOLTS TO BRING THE BODY BACK TO LIFE.

... AND A NEW SUPERSKINHEED EMERGED.

EURRGH!!

THE REJUVINATED HUNK FELT A STRANGE URGE TO LEAVE THE LAB. HE WAS CONFUSED.....

..... BUT NOT TOO CONFUSED

WHEN I WAS YOUR AGE, SONNY JIM,...

KRAK!

ARE YOU SURE?

THE LOCAL POLICE WERE SOON ALERTED...

... BUT NOT QUITE QUICKLY ENOUGH

UH?

HI! GUESS WHAT. IT'S...

...PIG BASHIN' TIME

COPPA!

BAP!

SCUFFA!

KWHAM!!

CRUMBS! THIS BRUTE IS WACKING ME OUT THE WINDOW!!!

CD 13.1.81

NOW THAT SKINHEED HAS RETURNED, INSANE, BULLET PROOF AND WITH UNHUMAN STRENGTH, HOW CAN HE BE STOPPED? NEXT ISSUE: VIOLENCE SPECIAL

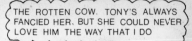

George & Linda

"...Ciggies and BEER"...

— Martin 1981 —

Wa's friends are for...eh!

and yewl never walk a-a-lone...!

Happy New Year!

HECK
BLECH
BLOOG

STROLL ON!

HOW ABOUT A CUPPA MR. FENCE?

YES, AND DO HAVE A SWEETIE

THANKS VERY MUCH

JOKE

A man treating his fence with creosote

CREOSOTE

Vince Valentino — The Ladykiller

URP!

RATATATA TATATAT!

THE END

THE RETURN OF MR. KIPPLIN

AFTER MY VISIT TO MR. KIPPLIN'S I HAD INVITED HIM ROUND FOR TEA AND CAKE. I FELT POORLY SO TOOK ASPRIN.

Johnny Shiloe 1981

BUT IT WAS TO NO AVAIL...

FOR I OPENED THE DOOR ONLY TO FLING MY GUTS AT HIM.

ARE YOU NOT WELL?

professor piehead

Johnny Spike 2·7·81

'EIGHT BALL' JOE

CD 11.79

JOE WAS A REAL 'DUMBO'

HE TRIED TO EAT WITH HIS EARS AT MEALTIMES...

AND HE WOULD ENJOY MAKING LARGE HOLES IN THE FLOOR AT HOME...

HE COULD WALK FOR TEN MILES WITH NO HANDS.....

AND HE ALWAYS LIED TO HIS AUNTIE ELSIE ABOUT HIS DATE OF BIRTH.

ON BANK HOLIDAYS, JOE WOULD PRETEND TO BE A STATUE.....

AND HE OFTEN ASKED FOR KIPPERS AT THE BUTCHERS.'

ON HIS 21ST BIRTHDAY HIS DAD HAD HIM CERTIFIED AND LOCKED UP. HE WAS VERY EXCITED...

AND HE LIVED VERY HAPPILY EVER AFTER IN A HOLE IN THE HOSPITAL FLOOR.

O L D ✳ J O K E ✳ ✳ ✳ ✳ ✳ ✳ ✳ ✳ ✳ ✳ ✳ ✳ ✳ ✳ ✳ ✳ ✳

Darling

Yes darling?

I've got something to tell you darling

What's that darling?

Darling, I'm going to have a baby

Don't you think you've eaten enough already darling?

BIZ 81

Terror On Platform 13

A violent nightmare in Blood!

Platform 13 was an isolated oil rig 100 miles off the coast of Scotland. For several weeks the crew had heard terrifying noises coming from the deep dark waters below them, and in a series of late night attacks security guards had suffered broken noses as they stood guard over the rig.

KNUT!

AAAAGHH!!!

Rumour had it that a huge beast was at large beneath the platform.
Then, one cold winter evening, as the workers were relaxing in the bar, they heard a chilling scream from outside, and then the room began to shake. A large claw pierced the wall...

WAM!

I'll have a bottle o'Bells or you'll have or broken nose, pal!

Bllluddy Hell! Y-y-y-yes, sir!

It was the GIANT RAT!!!!

There's nowt like a game o'arrows, eh pal? What do y'reckon, Jimmy?

Please be careful M-m-m-ister rat

Will you shut up Jimmy, or I'll put y' in a box!

No sooner than the giant rat had appeared, private detective Ted Dempster was on his way to Scotland, armed with a bottle of whisky. But this was no ordinary bottle of whisky. It was a special bottle of whisky topped up with a deadly combination of shampoo and rat poison.

Going to Scotland?

Yeah, hop on

CD 6/81

Minutes later the cunning Dempster was mingling with the terrified workers in the bar when the rat arrived for his evening drink...

Giz a fuckin whisky 'n I'll no be payin'!

Why don't you join me mister? I've got whisky to share.

That's very kind of y', pal, but I don't think I like the shape o'your nose!

KNUT!

Amazingly, Dempster was unscathed despite the rat's violent heeder. As he bundled the bully away, he explained why...

The rat drank my whisky which contained very special shampoo, which, when taken internally, produces an instant curly perm. The rat's new hairdo absorbed all the power from his butt, leaving me unharmed!

THE END

MICKEY WAS HOPPING HIS WAY HOME FROM SCHOOL ONE DAY, WHEN HE CAME ACROSS A STRANGE OBJECT...

BY THE WRATH OF THE MIGHTY MARTIAN GODS! IT WAS A BIG SPACE ROCKET!

MICKEY HOPPED AROUND THE LARGE ROCKET FOR A WHILE, BEFORE HE FOOLISHLY CLIMBED INTO THE BIG CABIN...

BEFORE HE KNEW IT, MICKEY HAD PRESSED THE WRONG BUTTON, AND HE WAS WHISKED AWAY BY THE MONSTER MACHINE!

MICKEY COULD BUT SIT AND WAIT...

AFTER WHAT SEEMED A VERY LONG TIME INDEED, THE ROCKET CRASHED...

MICKEY, WHO WAS KNOCKED UNCONCIOUS, WOKE SUDDENLY.

HE WAS IN THE HOUSE OF MR. 'EATING' CHARLESWORTH, WHO PROCEEDED TO VIOLENTLY VOMIT ON HIS FACE...

ROGER MELLIE

HELLO, GOOD EVENING AND WELCOME

THE MAN ON THE TELLY

IT'S A BUSY DAY FOR ROGER. HE'S GOT A MEETING AT T.V. CENTRE

AH HELLO ROGER. THIS IS MR WEST, HEAD OF DOCUMENTARIES

YES. WE WERE JUST THINKING ABOUT A TITLE FOR YOUR NEW SERIES, ROGER

BUT I THOUGHT WE'D ALREADY SETTLED ON "BASTARD WORLD IN ACTION"...

ERM. NO ROGER..

WELL, I THINK WE DECIDED THAT WAS A BIT TOO SIMILAR TO 'WORLD IN ACTION' ON I.T.V., ACTUALLY

YEAH, I SEE WHAT YOU MEAN. HMM! DIFFICULT ISN'T IT.... HOW ABOUT 'PANOR-FUCKING-RAMA' THEN?

NO ROGER. GAVIN AND I WERE THINKING THAT WE SHOULD CHOOSE A TITLE WHICH FITS THE SHOW...

AND I THINK WE DECIDED ON 'UK TODAY'! IT'S SIMPLE AND HAS A CATCHY RHYME TO IT AS WELL!

... SO DOES 'ARSEHOLE NEWS AND BASTARD VIEWS'. HOW ABOUT THAT GAVIN?

NO, SORRY ROGER. WE DON'T WANT ANYTHING VULGAR. IT'S AN EARLY EVENING SHOW. A NEWS DOCUMENTARY, Y'KNOW. I THINK WE SHOULD TRY TO KEEP IT CLEAN, OKAY

OH YEAH! OF COURSE. I CAN SEE THAT...

SO WHY NOT JUST KEEP IT SIMPLE? HOW ABOUT 'CUNT'?

I THINK YOU'D BETTER GO TO THE STATION CONTROLLER'S OFFICE, ROGER. HE WANT'S TO SEE YOU.

HMM!

I THINK IT'S ABOUT LAST NIGHTS NEWS HEADLINES. HE'S HAD SOME COMPLAINTS. WE'LL SORT THIS TITLE OUT LATER.

LATER...

YOU WANTED TO SEE ME? I SUPPOSE IT'S ABOUT THE SHODDY CAMERA WORK ON LAST NIGHTS NEWS. WE OUGHT TO GET SOMETHING DONE ABOUT IT...

CONTROLLERS OFFICE

NO ROGER. I'VE GOT A COMPLAINT HERE FROM 10 DOWNING STREET. IT'S ABOUT SOMETHING YOU SAID. I DON'T SUPPOSE THE PHRASE "MARGARET TWATTING THATCHER" RINGS A BELL?

SKINHEED

8

THE UNSTOPABLE FORCE!!!
AS SEEN ON TV

IN THE LAST ISSUE, SKINHEED, THE UNDEAD BEAST WITH A PSYCHO BRAIN AND UNHUMAN STRENGTH, WAS HEADING FOR LONDON!!

YES SIR! BOMB LONDON. I'LL SEE TO IT RIGHT AWAY!

SO FAR ALL ATTEMPTS TO STOP HIM HAD FAILED, SO THE ARMY DECIDED TO BOMB LONDON...

BOOM!

...AND THE 'H' BOMB FELL!

SADLY, THE MILITARY HAD BOMBED LONDON PREMATURELY. SKINHEED HAD NOT ARRIVED.

OH DEAR! I THINK WE'VE JUMPED THE GUN A LITTLE! HE HASN'T ARRIVED YET!!

AND WHEN HE DID ARRIVE, HE FOUND LONDON IN RUINS.

AS SKINHEED ROAMED THE RUINED CITY, THE ARMY WERE LAYING FRESH PLANS TO RID THE PLANET OF THIS DEAD BIG MUTANT OF A BOOT BOY

SORRY TO DISTURB YOU MINISTER. I'M AFRAID WE'VE BLOWN UP LONDON AND WE MAY HAVE TO DETONATE THE EARTH'S CORE...

OH DEAR... AND IT HASN'T WORKED... HMMM.... WELL WHY NOT STEER THE EARTH INTO THE PATH OF THE SUN. THAT SHOULD DO THE TRICK!!

AND SO LEADING ARMY SCIENTISTS LOWER A BOMB TO THE EARTHS CORE...

THE FORCE FROM THIS BOMB WILL CAUSE THE EARTH TO COLLIDE WITH THE SUN, KILLING THAT MONSTER IN ONE BIG BANG!

AT LAST WE'VE GOT HIM! THAT WILL BE HIS LAST CIGARETTE BEFORE THE END OF THE EARTH...AND HIM!!

bang!

WILL SKINHEED SURVIVE THIS MASSIVE BLAST? WILL THE EARTH BUMP INTO THE SUN? LOOK OUT FOR THE NEXT ISSUE
-SKINHEED IN SPACE!

'EIGHT BALL' JOE MK II

JOE LIVES IN A HOLE IN A HOSPITAL FLOOR...

HE USED TO CLOSE HIS EYES SO THE DOCTORS COULDN'T SEE HIM, AND...

HE TOLD ALL THE MICE THAT HE WAS A POP STAR

COR!! IS THAT SO MR ANT?

...AND THEN NOT LISTEN WHEN THEY TOLD HIM.

I SAID 10.15!! IT'S 10.15!!!

AND THIS UPSET PEOPLE

TIE A YELLOW RIBBON...

SOMETIMES HE WOULD ASK PEOPLE THE TIME...

EVERY OTHER SATURDAY HE WOULD CALL THE FIRE BRIGADE...... AND ASK THEM FOR A LIGHT.

GONE FISHING

SOMETIMES HE PRETENDS HE HAS GONE ON HOLIDAY...

GONE FISHING

AND THEN MAKES FACES AT PEOPLE WHEN THEY AREN'T LOOKING.

ONE DAY HE MARRIED A MOUSE AND THEY LIVED HAPPILY EVER AFTER.

VICTOR PRATT ★ THE STUPID TWAT ★

HELP ME VIC, I'M FALLING!

YOUR PULLIN' ME LEG!

MRS MAYBEE & HER CRAZY BABY

"MAYBEE WE SHOULD GO TO THE SHOPS!"

"LET'S FUCK A COPPA!"

BIFFA BACON

I'M OFF OUT DAD, T'CLOBBA SOMEONE IN THE MUSH

GIVE THE BASTARD ONE FROM ME, KIDDA

IN THE PARK...

UH?

WHO THE FUCK ARE YOU LOOKIN' AT?

BIFF!

GOT HIM...

BIFFA'S MUM

ER, HELLO MUM!

ARE Y'TALKIN' TO ME OR CHEWIN' A BRICK, SON...

'COS Y'LOSE Y'FUKKIN' TEETH BOTH WAYS

HOOF!

45

professor piehead

SWANT

SPECIAL WEAPONS AND NO TACTICS
DIVISION

FILL ME IN, ROGERS, I WANNA KNOW THE SCORE!

WE GOT A FRUITCAKE HOLDIN' SOME CHICK IN THAT SHED, SARGE!

SOUNDS LIKE A 507; HOSTAGE SITUATION

THIS CALLS FOR DIPLOMACY...

HEY, MUTHA FUKKA!

YOU'D BETTER HAUL YOUR ASS THE HELL OUTTA THERE!!!

OKAY, BUT HOW DO I KNOW YOU AIN'T GONNA SHOOT?

SHOOT!!?!

KRAKA! KRAKA!

BAM! BAM! BAM!

RATTA! TAT TAT!

PING! WHIZZ ZIP!

GEE MISTER, THAT WAS GREAT! CAN YOU GET MY CAT OUTTA THE TREE?

YAH! BREAK OUT THE HARDWARE ROGERS!!

SIR!!

LET'S ROLL!

NEXT ISSUE: S.W.A.N.T. KICK ASS!

MR. LOGIC

SUCH IS MY NAME, THEREFORE ONE CAN ASSUME THAT THIS COMIC STRIP IS IN SOME WAY ABOUT ME

HE'S A PAIN IN THE ARSE.

IN THE PUB

SEVENTY-TWO, LUVVA.

PARDON?

SEVENTY-TWO... FOR YOUR PINT LUV.

"SEVENTY-TWO FOR MY PINT"? I PRESUME THIS MUST BE SOME KIND OF A FINANCIAL DEAL I AM BEING OFFERED, UNFORTUNATELY SHE HAS NOT STATED WHICH FORM OF CURRENCY SHE REQUIRES.

SHE ALSO SEEMS TO BE UNDER SOME MENTAL STRESS, FOR SHE SEEMS TO THINK I AM HER LOVER. THIS IS NOT THE TRUTH. hmm

NEVERTHELESS SHE IS QUITE ATTRACTIVE, I SHALL MAKE INQUIRIES ABOUT HER SEXUAL ASPIRATIONS, AND HOPE THAT OUR FINANCIAL QUIBBLE WILL BE SORTED OUT IN THE RESULTING CONVERSATION.

WOULD YOU CARE TO INDULGE IN SEXUAL INTERCOURSE WITH ME? I HAVE A MODERATLEY LARGE PENIS.

SMASH! THUD! BANG! CRACK! AAAGH! WALLOP! BONK!

hmmm, YES, PHYSICAL VIOLENCE. NOT OVERALL AN ENJOYABLE SORT OF EXPERIENCE. I WONDER IF MY BEHAVIOR HAS IN SOME WAY PRECIPITATED THIS AGGRESSIVE RESPONSE.

LATER HAVE YOU THE TIME? I HAVE NEGLECTED TO DON MY WRIST CHRONOGRAPH.

EH? Y'WANT Y'FUCKIN' HEAD KICKED IN?!

hmm. A SEEMINGLY FRUITLESS EXERCISE.

BOOT!

FINISH.

49

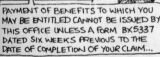

PRISONER of LOVE

CD/IS

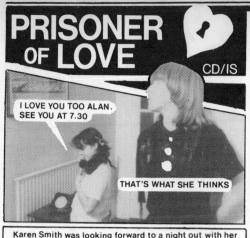

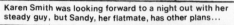

Karen Smith was looking forward to a night out with her steady guy, but Sandy, her flatmate, has other plans...

continued on p.54

Written in lipstick on wet toilet paper, the note told of how Karen had been kept prisoner in her own toilet for two months, while the boy she loved was stolen from her.

As Alan read it out aloud, Sandy realised the game was over. They finished the meal in silence before Alan rushed back to the flat...

professor Piehead

THE COMING OF THE EXECUTIONER

Shiloe·CD'82

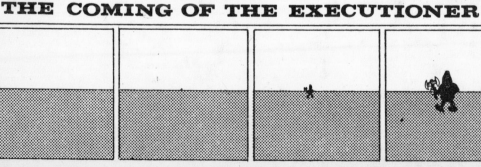

WELL,... I'M HERE.

55

THE PHANTOM OF THE BASTARD OPERA

CD 82ish — THE END

MRS MAYBEE & HER CRAZY BABY

SAMMY AND HIS STAMMER

FRANK

THE PRINCESS

ALAN WAS A BONNY YOUNG PRINCE...

GO AND SHITE!

ALAN'S DAD, KING DEREK, SAID IT WAS TIME FOR HIM TO FIND A WIFE...

SO OFF HE SET, IN SEARCH OF A BEAUTIFUL YOUNG PRINCESS...

WHAT THE FUCK..?

HE TRIED KISSING A FROG OR TWO...

BUT HE THOUGHT HE'D ONLY CATCH SOMETHING, BESIDES, HE WAS GETTING SOME PRETTY ODD LOOKS

SO HE TRIED LEAVING HIS SHOE ON THE STAIRS..

BUT NOBODY CAME TO TRY IT ON AT MIDNIGHT, OR ANYTHING, AND EVENTUALLY THE COUNCIL CAME TO TAKE IT AWAY...

COME BACK, YOU ROTTEN BASTARD!

REFUSE COLLECTION DEPT.

EVENTUALLY ALAN MET FRANK WHO WASN'T REALLY A PRINCESS, BUT HE SAID HE'D PRETEND IF THE PAY WAS ALL RIGHT...

ERM...

SO ALAN WENT TO SEE KING DEREK AND TELL HIM HE WAS GOING TO MARRY FRANK

KING DEREK WAS NOT AMUSED...

POOF!

AND HE BROKE ALAN'S NOSE WITH A HAMMER.

SMACK!

WHO IS HE? WHERE DOES HE COME FROM? NOBODY KNOWS THE SECRET OF...

The BROWN BOTTLE

IT'S A QUIET EVENING IN THE CITY. MILD MANNERED REPORTER, BARRY BROWN IS WALKING HOME WHEN...

WINEYS
WINES & BOOZE

HMMM... AN OFF LICENSE

CD 10-82

BROWN DASHES TO A NEARBY CALL BOX...

TELEPHONE

AND SECONDS LATER...

A DYNAMIC FIGURE EMMERGES...

DOWN ME FUCKIN' NECK EH? CHEERS, Y'F-F-F-FUCKERS!

HIC!

HOWAY THEN... Y-Y-BASTARDS I'LL F-F-F-FUCKIN' TAKE THE LOT OF YER... HIC...

HOWAY Y'BASTARD... GIZ A F-F-F-FUCKIN' BORREL OF BROWN... HERE... LOOK.. I'VE GOT THE M-M-MONEY MAN

HOWAY MAN W-W-WILL YA... HIC...

I'VE TOLD YOU BEFORE BAZ, I'M NOT SERVING YOU IN HERE.

DIVN'T GIVE US THAT Y'B... BASTARD! I'M F-F-F-FUCKIN DEAD SOBER...

I'VE NOT... I'VE HAD NOWT T-T-DRINK MAN... I'VE NEVER HAD N-N-NOWT!

SHIT... I'VE D-DROPPED ME F-F-FUCKIN' TABS H.. H... HOARRGH!!!

OKAY SON, LET'S GO

I'M FUCKIN' GOING NOWHERE... I'VE DONE N-N-NOWT!

HAVE YOU GOT A... A... A LIGHT THERE PAL?... HIC...

READ & LEARN
WITH NAYLOR HAMMOND, Bsc.

CD 3·83

TELEVISION

As you probably know, every day millions of people take famous television programmes like 'The Archers' for granted. But it wasn't very long ago that people were finding it impossible to imagine life as we know it today without the television.

It all began with Alexander Graham Bell's imortal words, "Can you hear me Livingstone?" Television had been born and within days it had become a household object.

But early TV programmes were crude affairs. Indeed the radio as it was then known was similar to the telephone in that it didn't have a picture. Hence the nickname 'Talkies' which refered to the early broadcasts like Kenneth Wolstenhome and Charlie Chaplin.

The first TV pictures were a far cry from the colourful ones we see on today's silver screen. At one time all programmes had to be made in black and white, making it difficult for snooker players to distinguish between different balls. Television played a major role in the Battle Of Britain (starring Michael Caine) when 'Radar', (a kind of army television) enabled submarines to go underneath the water for long periods at a time.

Z Cars was probably the first programme ever to appear on TV. Since then there have of course been many others, including Dr Who, The News and Blue Peter. But according to viewing figures (people who watch television all the time) the most successful programme ever is The Mousetrap. The longest running breakfast cereal ever, it features Albert Tatlock, Elsie Tanner and co. in the everyday story of Brookside, a ficticious motel built especially for television by the people who actually live there.

Nowerdays modern inventions like the satellite, (a kind of flying space television) are appearing in living rooms across the world. The growing popularity of micro-chips and other convenience foods such as Breakfast TV, TV Snacks and the electrically powered 'Cable' TV (which uses complicated wires to obtain a bigger picture), have revolutionised television design.

Now, and with the advent of the space age, 'E.T.' and 'Space Invaders' are replacing the older televisions in many homes. However, a useful magazine called 'TV Times' is now available to people interested in televisions. It contains colour pictures and is available from most newsagents priced 35 pence.

See you next time !

Naylor Hammond.
BSc.

Love is Blind

Photographed entirely with a camera by Dave Phillipson. Processed and printed by QCL. © Viz Lurv Album 1983 CD

PAUL WHICKER

WHO IS NO LONGER A VICAR, BUT IS DEFINATELY STILL TALL.

THAT'S RIGHT! IT'S ME! I BET YOU THOUGHT YOU'D GOT RID OF ME! WELL..... YOU WERE FUCKIN' WRONG!!!

FROM TIME TO TIME, YOU MAY FIND YOURSELF..ER .. BETWEEN APPOINTMENTS AS I DID RECENTLY AFTER CLOCKING THE BISHOP ON THE SNOTBOX... I'M NOT SAYING THAT IT WASN'T WORTH IT TO SLAP THE OLD GIT...

BUT IT LEFT ME WITH A PROBLEM... VIS A VIS BEER MONEY. TO THIS END, I HAULED MY ASS DOWN TO THE D.H.S.S. TO CLAIM WHAT WAS RIGHTFULLY MINE... 'NOT SO EASY' Y'MIGHT SAY - AN'YOU'D BE RIGHT!

I'M AFRAID YOU'LL HAVE TO WAIT IN THE QUEUE IF YOU WANT TO CLAIM UNEMPLOYMENT BENEFIT.

NEW CLAIMS

SEE WHAT I MEAN?

THIS CALLS FOR ACTION!

HOW WOULD YOU LIKE ME TO STICK MY FINGER DOWN MY THROAT AND FETCH UP MY DINNER ALL OVER YOUR NICE COUNTER?

WELL, REALLY... IF YOU INSIST ON BEING ABUSIVE I WILL CALL THE SUPERVISOR...

ABUSIVE? YOU AI'NT HEARD NOTHIN' YET YOU FOUR-EYED PISS-POT!

IN THE SUPERVISOR'S OFFICE...
NOW THEN, WHAT SEEMS TO BE THE TROUBLE?

WELL, SINCE YOU ASK, FAT MAN, I'LL TELL YOU. THE PUBS OPEN IN HALF AN HOUR AND I HAVEN'T GOT A RED CENT WITH WHICH TO OIL MY GIZZARD...

PLUS... I'VE GOT A DATE WITH A RED-HOT DAME, AND I CAN HARDLY EXPECT HER TO DROP HER KEX IF SHE HAS TO PAY FOR HER OWN LIQUOR

AS YOU CAN SEE, YOU HAVE TO KNOW HOW TO HANDLE THESE FUCKERS, OR THEY'LL HAVE YOU RUNNING AROUND LIKE A BLUE-ARSED FLY...

CHEEKY TWAT!

B.A.F.

I FIND THIS VERY HARD TO BELIEVE, BUT YOUR APPLICATION STATES THAT YOU WERE A VICAR, AND AS SUCH WE CAN PAY YOU NO BENEFIT SINCE THE CHURCH IS A CHARITY, AND YOU PAID NO NATIONAL INSURANCE...

BAM!

WAT?! THEN I AM VERY MUCH AFRAID I SHALL HAVE TO KICK YOUR LUNGS OUT!

PICK THE BONES OUT OF THAT ONE CUNT-BUBBLE!

AAAAAH BY DOSE!

SMACK!

SAME AS IT EVER WAS, EH READERS?

MR. LOGIC

SUCH IS MY NAME, SO THEREFORE ONE CAN ASSUME THAT THIS COMIC STRIP IS IN SOME WAY ABOUT ME

HE'S A PAIN IN THE ARSE.

IN THE POST OFFICE
DO YOU SELL POSTAGE STAMPS?
OF COURSE!

HOW MANY DO YOU WANT?

I DO NOT NECCESSARILY REQUIRE ANY. I MERELY ASKED WHETHER OR NOT YOU SOLD POSTAGE STAMPS

HOWEVER I DO AT PRESENT REQUIRE ONE FIRST CLASS STAMP.

THAT'S 16 p PLEASE.

YOU ASSUME THAT I WISH TO MAKE A PURCHASE...
?

I MERELY STATED THAT I REQUIRED A STAMP, A PURCHASE DOES NOT NECCESSARILY FOLLOW.

HOWEVER, I DO AT THIS POINT INTEND TO PURCHASE THE STAMP. ACCORDINGLY REMIT THE SUM OF 16 NEW PENCE.

ARE YOU FINISHED YET, SMART ARSE?

MY FINANCIAL TRANSACTION IS COMPLETE, BUT MY NAME IS NOT "SMART ARSE"..

I WAS CHRISTENED...
KNUT!
UGH!
FIN.

BILLY BOGGLES

THE KID INVENTOR

TOMMY IS ENTERING THE BBC YOUNG SCIENTIST OF THE YEAR COMPETITION
NOW THEN, I'LL JUST MAKE A COUPLE OF SMALL ADJUSTMENTS TO THIS RADIO

FIRST I'LL REPLACE THIS ELECTRIC BIT WITH A SMALL MOUSE...

THEN AFFIX A PAIR OF ORDINARY SCISSORS TO THIS LONG WIRE BIT...

AND THERE WE HAVE IT! A MOUSE SCISSOR RADIO!

A TOTAL SUCCESS! NOW FOR MY NEXT EXPERIMENT...
...TO REPLACE MY HEAD WITH A COLOUR TELEVISION

FIRST I WILL REMOVE MY HEAD...
SAW

BOBBY CHARLTON OBE

BIRD SHITE

THIS CAR IS COVERED IN SHITE

BLEEDIN' BIRDS! THEY ALWAYS PICK ON MY CAR

RADIO '83

POP!

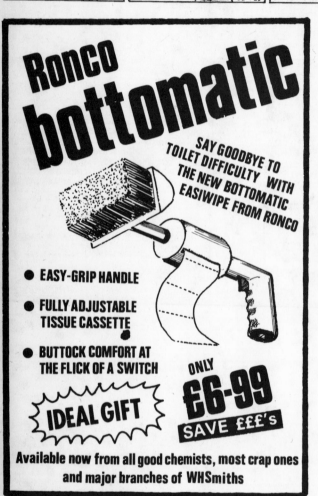

miserable sod

ZOO OF SHAME

EXCLUSIVE

Animals make love as children watch

Our reporters have investigated a disturbing behind the scenes sex scandal at a leading London zoo.

And we have proof that staff at the zoo in Regents Park have actually encouraged sex between animals.

On a recent visit to the zoo we watched as penguins made love openly while visitors, some of them young children, passed nearby. And we witnessed giraffes attempting sex as zoo keepers looked on.

Lizard

In the reptile house the temperature was noticably high, and we saw lizards and snakes romp naked in the grass.

Passion

Nearby a crowd watched as lions explored each others bodies, while in the next cage leopards were preparing for a night of passion.

Sin

It seems that such acts of shame are an everyday occurence at this, the zoo of sin. And staff there have been actively involved in encouraging sex between animals.

> ### A VIZ INVESTIGATION

We can reveal that the zoo's top attraction Chi Chi the giant panda is a key figure in an international sex syndicate involving well known zoos in China and the USA. Our investigations revealed that the bear is regularly taken out of the country to other zoos where it is encouraged to take part in steamy sex sessions with other pandas.

Head

Yesterday the zoo's head keeper was not prepared to discuss claims. But when we confronted him with our dossier of evidence, including photographs of a young rabbit having sex, we were told to piss off.

This woman sold children ice cream while animals had sex.

The BBC were quick to scotch rumours today that children's TV presenter Keith Chegwin is an African tree lizard.

The rumours, which came from an undisclosed source, suggested that Chegwin spent all of his spare time eating locusts caught with his long tongue, and that he had also laid eggs in the Blue Peter tree outside the Television Centre.

A spokesman for the BBC said: "Chegwin is not a lizard", and later added: "Go away – Chegwin is not a lizard. No comment".

Big tits!

Shapely Joanna Jones has got a massive pair of assets.

Said Joanna's mother: "I always knew she would go places – she's certainly got the credentials".

Melons

Joanna's boyfriend, photographer Tony Lewis told us that when Joanna goes shopping, she rarely forgets the melons! "She always comes in with a nice pair", he added.

Knockers

When our reporter called, Joanna's bell was out of order. Lucky thing she had a big pair of knockers!

Professor Piehead

OKAY JOE, ALL SET TO TEST MY NEW HEAT SEEKING MISSILE?

HSM MK.I.

THE MISSILE

WUMP!

WOOSH !!

HSM MK.I.

CD 5·84

Captain Incontinent

AH HAA!!

VICTOR PRATT THE STUPID TWAT

MONEY MAKES THE WORLD GO ROUND, VIC

BUT SURELY IT'S ALWAYS BEEN ROUND

JS·CD 4·83

Rude Kid... COME AND WASH YOUR HANDS BEFORE DINNER YOUNG MAN!

FUCK FUCK FUCK FUCK FUCK.. FUCK FUCK FUCK **FUCK!**

prof. piehead

OKAY JOE, ALL SET TO DROP A TON WEIGHT ON MY NEW CRASH HELMET

TIM THE ASSISTANT

ONE TON WEIGHT (ATTACHED TO TOP OF LADDER)

TIM THE ASSISTANT'S PAIR OF STEP LADDERS, TO WHICH THE WEIGHT IS ATTATCHED.

SURE THING, BOSS

PAF!!

CD 13·2·81

BIFFA BACON AND PERCY POSH

AH! PERCY POSH IS PLAYING HOPSCOTCH

HE'LL NOT MIND IF I BUTT IN...

HI PERCY!

K-THUD!

UMPH!

HO HO!

THAT LITTLE WHEEZE NEVER FAILS.

LATER...

AH HA!

THIS 2×12 HEAVY DUTY TIMBER PLANK GIVES ME AN IDEA!

HAVE I GOT A SURPRISE FOR PERCY!

HIYA PERCY

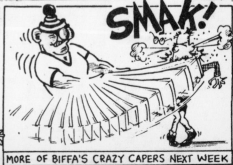

SMAK!

MORE OF BIFFA'S CRAZY CAPERS NEXT WEEK

74

TALKING SENSE

Charlie Pontoon

The column that pulls no punches

How can the government justify spending billions on nuclear weapons when they tell us they aren't intending to use them? If I spent a fraction of that amount on fireworks, my kids would make bloody sure they got set off.

So come on Maggie. Light the fuses, and we'll give the reds a display they're never gonna forget.

And who the hell are CND? They tell us everyone in Switzerland has got a bomb shelter. That figures. Last time the shit hit the fan they were all hiding in their bloody bank vaults, leaving us to deal with the hun.

It's all well and good aiming bombs at Russia, but anyone who knows their history will tell you it's the French who are the real trouble makers.

So come on Maggie. Let's show them frogs what they can do with their butter mountains.

Jimmy Hill tells us that football hooliganism is killing the game. So what's he gonna do about it? Talking on the telly isn't going to help.

Come on Jimmy. Get down on the terraces next Saturday and give them hooligans a hiding they're never gonna forget.

And who does Bobby Robson think he's kidding? His team couldn't score in a brothel with ten pound notes tied around their choppers.

Isn't it about time we gave the bobby on the beat a shooter? Let's face it, kids will be kids, and someone's always gonna be taking pot shots at the Old Bill. Why not get the coppers tooled up, so at least they can take a few villains with 'em when they go.

CROSS THE BALL

No. 1 PORTSMOUTH V CRYSTAL PALACE 6th November 1952
Conditions: windy but warm, with the possibility of a shower later on.

The ball has been obliterated from the above picture. Using your skill and judgement, and the information provided, make a cross with a three-quarter inch chisel tip permanent marker where you think the exact centre of the ball is. Each entry is allowed a minimum of ten crosses.

Fill in the attached coupon and send it together with £25 cash to 'Cross The Ball', c/o Room 37, The Old Station Hotel, Birmingham, as soon as possible.

I enclose £25.00 cash.

5·84

Signed _____

SPIDER JOKE

76

WORD GAME

Can you think of 1000 words or more?
Remember, each word must be of four letters or more, and can only be used once, e.g. apple. Send your list to 'Goal Of The Month', Match Of The Day, BBC TV, London W1A 4WW.

READ & LEARN | *with Naylor Hammond Bsc.*

This week Naylor has some interesting facts about

Botany

As you probably know, Botany first arrived in England by ship, perhaps the earliest example being the beautiful Mary Rose. Nowadays we rely on botany to provide us with coffee, tea and many popular brands of cigarettes. For all of these, together with pipe tobacco and cigars, grow on trees alongside fruit, nuts and chocolate.

A Pipe

There are of course three main types of botany: Zoology – the botany of animals; Biology – the botany of things that grow on trees; and archeology – another kind of botany.

We are all familiar with flowers which are often yellow and grow in our gardens. But all flowers must eventually grow into large trees, and this complicated 'life cycle' (a botanical form of transport) has fascinated botaneers for many years.

A Cow

Sir Richard Attenborough shocked the botany world with his theory 'you are what you eat'. He discovered that cows eat flowers, which turn into vegetables. Man eats cows *with* vegetables, and so the 'food chain' continues. Latter day food chains include Fine Fare and Sainsburys.

Animals live in the jungle which is in Africa. This so-called 'Animal Kingdom' is largely made up of three types of species: Fish – a kind of underwater mammal; Mammals – such as reptiles; and vegetables.

A Tree

Vegetables are a kind of underground fruit which live in the soil and drink minerals such as pepsi and cresta. Vegetables provide us with our butter, margarine and even cosmetic products (a kind of space food).

A Vegetable

Since the sixties flower power era botany has become a popular leisure activity. Small flowers, vegetables and useful information about trees can be obtained from larger branches of the Post Office.

See you next time *Naylor Hammond Bsc.*

LUCKY FRANK

HMM! I FEEL LUCKY! I THINK I'LL GO FOR A WALK

SOON
I BOUGHT THIS GIFT FOR A FRIEND WHOM I NOW DISLIKE. PLEASE WILL YOU HAVE IT INSTEAD
TOTAL STRANGER →

OH DEAR. IT IS ONLY AN OLD VASE.
I'LL GIVE IT TO MY MOTHER

LATER
THANKYOU VERY MUCH. THIS VASE IS VERY LOVELY.
INDEED IT IS! HAPPY CHRISTMAS, MUM

THEN...
FRANK'S UNCLE TED, THE ACCOMPLISHED HISTORIAN.
THIS IS AN EGYPTIAN VASE - WORTH OVER A THOUSAND POUNDS!

ONE THOUSAND POUNDS! AND IT'S ALL MINE. HOW FORTUNATE

OH YOINKS!! THAT VASE WAS VERY VALUABLE AND I GAVE IT AWAY!
HOW COULD I BE SO UNLUCKY?

LATER...
YOPP! MUM'S DEAD!!

THAT'S RIGHT. THE VASE CARRIES A FATAL EGYPTIAN CURSE! IT'S A LUCKY THING YOU GAVE IT AWAY
PHEW!
IT CERTAINLY IS!

I'M FROM THE INSURANCE COMPANY. YOU GET £50,000 COS YOUR MOTHER DIED. AND I'LL GIVE YOU FIVE THOUSAND FOR THIS PRETTY VASE!
YOINKS! IT MUST BE MY LUCKY DAY!!!
THE END

AT FULCHESTER STADIUM, TEAM COACH SYD PRESTON HAD BAD NEWS FOR UNITED BOSS TOMMY BROWN...

HALF MAN, HALF FISH, YOUNG KEEPER BILLY THOMSON WAS SET TO SIGN FOR FULCHESTER UNITED. BUT GUS PARKER, THE GRIMTHORPE CITY BOSS HAD OTHER PLANS FOR BILLY...

CD 1/84

HAVE YOU READ THE PAPER TOMMY? THE YOUNG FISH KID HAS BEEN KIDNAPPED!

THE PAPER TOLD THE STORY...

EVENING PLANET
UNITED STAR KIDNAPPED!
FISH KEEPER VANISHES ON EVE OF DEBUT

THIS HAS TO BE THE WORK OF OUR ARCH RIVAL GUS PARKER, MANAGER OF NEIGHBOURING GRIMTHORPE CITY

YEAH, AND IT LEAVES US WITH LITTLE CHANCE IN SATURDAY'S ALL IMPORTANT DERBY!

MEANWHILE, AT THE GRIMTHORPE TRAINING CAMP, GUS PARKER IS PLANNING A DERBY DEFEAT FOR UNITED.

WHAT ARE WE GONNA DO TO THE FISH KID, BOSS?

NOTHING! ON SATURDAY BILLY THE FISH WILL LINE UP FOR FULCHESTER!

BUT IT WON'T BE THE REAL BILLY THOMSON! IT WILL BE THIS INFLATABLE REPLICA!

SO UNITED WILL BE PLAYING WITH A BALLOON IN GOAL – NO MATCH FOR OUR FORWARDS. THIS WAY WE CAN'T LOSE!

EXACTLY!

HA HA!

AND THERE'S NOTHING OUR FISH HEADED FRIEND CAN DO TO STOP US!

THE BIG DAY ARRIVED, AND AS KICK-OFF APPROACHED, THERE WAS STILL NO SIGN OF THE MISSING STAR...

IT LOOKS LIKE THIS NEW KID THOMSON ISN'T GONNA MAKE IT

YEAH

EAT CRISPS WATCH TELLY READ THE PA BUY DRINK BEER

BUT SUDDENLY A FIGURE EMMERGES FROM THE TUNNEL

HEY LOOK. IT'S BILLY THE FISH!

THIS NEW 'FISH LIKE' KEEPER HAS MADE IT AFTER ALL.

AND IN THE FULCHESTER DUG OUT, TOMMY BROWN BREATHES A SIGH OF RELIEF

I CAN'T BELIEVE IT! THOMSON MUST HAVE ESCAPED HIS CAPTORS WITH ONLY SECONDS TO SPARE

SOON THE GAME WAS UNDERWAY...

BLAST! I'VE BEEN BEATEN. BUT HE'LL NOT GET PAST BILLY THE FISH!

BUT, IN THE FULCHESTER GOAL...

OH NO! HE'S SCORED

THAT FISH KEEPER DIDN'T EVEN MOVE

BOO!

THIS NEW KID THOMSON IS A LOAD OF RUBBISH!

PUNT!

WILL GRIMTHORPE RUN RIOT OVER UNITED? WILL THE REAL BILLY THOMSON SAVE THE GAME, AND HIS OWN REPUTATION? FIND OUT IN THE NEXT EPISODE OF BILLY THE FISH

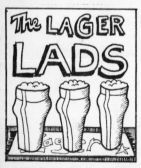

The LAGER LADS

HEY, LADS, LET'S GO IN THE NEW 'EL TUXEDO WINE BAR PALACE OF LEISURE' FOR SOME LAGER, EH?

AT THE CLUB

SORRY SON, YOUR SHOES AREN'T SMART ENOUGH.

BUT THEY'RE ITALIAN, THEY COST ME £200 FROM A TRENDY SHOP!

OH, SORRY, COME IN.

INSIDE

THREE STRAIGHT GLASSES, ERM, LAGER, AND, ERM... PINTS... STRAIGHT... AND... I'LL PAY FOR IT BY NAME... AND HE'S... ERM

THE LAGER'S OFF. I'LL GO AND PUT A NEW KEG ON.

IN THE CELLAR...

TEE-HEE CHUCKLE

PSSS

LAGER

IT'S GREAT MAN!

THE SMITHS

EXLUSIVE INTERVIEW

Morrissey (right) and the one with dark glasses, holding a tree.

The Smiths have certainly taken the pop world by storm in 1984.

So we dropped in to see them on their recent sell-out U.K. tour and took the opportunity to ask lead singer Morrissey how the group's unusual name came about. But he wouldn't talk to us.

LIVE

So we thought we'd turn the tables and ask some of the several thousand Smiths listed in the telephone directory what they thought of their pop namesakes.

TULIP

When we called Mr. J. Smith of London he told us he had never heard of the band, while Mr K. M. Smith of Reading said he had heard them on the radio but prefered to listen to the Beatles.

DRUGS

Mrs P. Smith of Manchester revealed that in recent weeks several people had dialed her number by mistake, and that she wasn't prepared to discuss her musical tastes over the telephone.

TOPLESS

A spokesman for W. H. Smiths in Newcastle offered to put us through to their record department who told us that the band's album was available on special offer, but refused to comment any further.

Several Smiths, including Mr H. Smith of Bristol, were not in when we called.

RIOT

With a successful tour behind them and the album flying high in the U.K. charts, 1984 looks set to continue as The Smiths year.

ARREST

For a final comment we asked painter and decorator Mr Alan Smith of Edinburgh whether he thought that the Smith's assault on the charts and dance floors of Britain would continue in the months ahead, and possibly spread to Europe and the U.S.A. After a moment's thought he said he wasn't sure, then he put the phone down.

ENEMY PLANE AT 1-O-CLOCK

RADIO '81

THAT'S GOOD, WE'VE GOT ½ AN HOUR TO SPARE, THEN

★ FRANKIE · FEEL ★
HE'S ALWAYS FEELING PEOPLES' TITS!

I BET YOU 50P I CAN FEEL YOUR TITS WITHOUT TAKING MY HANDS OUT OF MY POCKETS!

OKAY

WELL WORTH 50P I'LL SAY! CHORTLE!

GROPE!

END

What a crazy coincidence!

No long after we married my wife and I moved into a new house in Milton Keynes. Imagine our surprise to find our next door neighbours had a blue car — the very same colour as our own!

**Mrs. B. Jones
Milton Keynes**

* Write and tell us about your crazy coincidences. £5 paid for the best letter.

When it comes to shopping my three year old son Peter really takes the biscuit. I sent him to the corner shop to buy a loaf of bread and a packet of biscuits. Imagine my surprise when he returned carrying a boaf of lread and a backet of piscuits!

**Mrs. Ann Thomson
Essex**

Motorcyclist Mix-up

Early one morning I was awoken by a knock at the door. A passing motorcyclist had crashed into our garden fence and asked if she could use our phone.

We could hardly refuse. That motorcyclist was the Queen of England.

**Mrs. B. Baxter
Aberdeen**

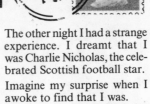

Our pet labrador 'Johnny' must be the most timid creature on Earth. Not only does he not bite the postman, he doesn't even bark very often.

**Miss S. Powell
Swansea**

Holiday Mix-up

In a crowded street I spotted a girl I thought was my fiancee, so I married her. Imagine my surprise when she turned around to find that she was a complete stranger. Luckily we both saw the funny side.

**J. Squires
Bolton**

Imagine my surprise when I awoke the other morning and it was 9.30. I had over-slept.

I wonder whether any other readers have had this experience?

**Miss L. Howe
Newcastle**

I am sure your readers are familiar with the expression 'you can't teach an old dog new tricks'. Well, I'm sure our labrador Goldie would disagree. Even though he isn't particularly old.

**Mrs. Ivy Jones
Devon**

The other night I had a strange experience. I dreamt that I was Charlie Nicholas, the celebrated Scottish football star.

Imagine my surprise when I awoke to find that I was.

**Charlie Nicholas
London**

How about a picture of some cows?

**P. Barker
Rotheram**

* Here you are. Let's hear any other suggestions readers have.

When I boarded a bus the other day I was sure I had seen the driver somewhere before.

I remembered where when he turned up on my doorstep that evening. He was my husband.

**Mrs. D. McArdle
Arbroath**

Marriage Mix-up

On our recent holiday in Majorca my husband and I ordered a bottle of red wine from the Spanish speaking waiter. Imagine our surprise when a returned carrying a bottle of white.

Never-the-less, we had a wonderful holiday and will be returning there next year.

**Mrs. K. Fowler
Derby**

In a crowded car park my husband and I were unable to find our car. We felt proper fools when, after three hours, we remembered we don't have one.

Luckily we both saw the funny side.

**Mrs. E. Rolands
Coventry**

It's a FUNNY WORLD

Compiled by Bob Liar

Players and spectators could hardly believe their eyes when they arrived for a fourth division match in Potizi, Bolivia. For the match referee, Mr Boco Perez, had arrived wearing his shorts back to front.

★ ★ ★

A cake factory worker in Argentina was sacked after customers complained of motorbikes in their cakes. Ricardo Gomez later told police how he hed stolen a total of 174 motorcycles and disposed of them by putting them in cakes.

★ ★ ★

Doctors in Chile could hardly believe their eyes when they examined X-rays of 56 year old traffic warden Enrico Parona. Inside him they found a total of 436 motor cars, weighing no less than 75 tons.

★ ★ ★

A court in Brazil recently fined a rest home owner the equivalent of £25 after hearing how he had sold old age pensioners for pet food.

Alfredo De Falcos told the court he had sold 33 residents to his brother's dog food factory by mistake.

Phoar!

★ Pretty Cindy Johnson, 24, certainly has got a big pair of jugs.

★ They've been turning heads ever since Cindy bought them while on holiday in Portugal.

RADIO/CD

DOCTOR, I'VE GOT A STOMACH UPSET

BOO! SOB!

I HATE YOU! I HATE YOU! I HATE YOU!

He Played On My Heartstrings

Ever since the day Tony White began playing guitar at the Tea Time Cafe customers had been flooding in. But Tony's girlfriend, waitress Cindy Johnson wasn't too happy...

BUSINESS IS BOOMING THANKS TO YOU, TONY. IF ONLY OLD MRS MORRIS WOULD PAY YOU FOR YOUR TROUBLES. SHE'S SUCH A MISER.

OH, FORGET IT CINDY. I JUST LOVE TO SING AND PLAY GUITAR.

STOP TALKING AND GET ON WITH YOUR WORK! PEOPLE NEED SERVING.

YES MRS MORRIS

Later, at closing time, Mrs Morris was counting the day's takings...

I'M AFRAID I'VE BROKEN ANOTHER STRING MRS MORRIS. I'VE ONLY GOT ONE LEFT NOW. COULD I POSSIBLY HAVE A FEW PENCE TO BUY SOME NEW ONES?

NO YOU CAN NOT! MONEY – IT'S ALL YOU PEOPLE EVER THINK ABOUT. WELL I CAN MANAGE PERFECTLY WELL WITHOUT YOU. YOU'RE FIRED!

Tony's future looked bleak...

OH DEAR. NOTHING TO PLAY ON, AND NOWHERE TO PLAY. WHAT WILL I DO?

That evening...

IF ONLY I HAD A DECENT GUITAR. THEN I COULD PLAY IN A BAND.

WE'LL WORK SOMETHING OUT TONY. I KNOW WE WILL.

LITTLE DOES TONY KNOW, I'VE BEEN SAVING MY TIPS. NOW I CAN AFFORD TO BUY HIM THE GUITAR HE'S ALWAYS WANTED.

Next day Cindy takes her savings and goes to buy the guitar.

IT WAS MORE EXPENSIVE THAN I'D THOUGHT, BUT TONY DESERVES IT.

OH NO! A CAR.

THERE GO MY SAVINGS, AND TONY'S HOPES OF A JOB. SOB, SOB.

I'M TERRIBLY SORRY BABE, I DIDN'T SEE YOU.

HEY! YOU'RE BILLY GEORGE, THE FAMOUS POP SINGER.

SHUCKS! I SEEM TO HAVE BROKEN YOUR GUITAR.

IT WAS MY BOYFRIEND'S ACTUALLY.

Cindy explained how Tony had lost his job playing in the Tea Time Cafe, and how she had saved up to buy him the guitar.

... AND SO HE'LL NEVER GET A JOB NOW.

HMMM. I'D LIKE TO MEET TONY. MAYBE I CAN HELP.

Continued on p.

They found Tony sitting in the Tea Time Cafe...

HI TONY. I'M BILLY GEORGE AND I'M RECORDING A NEW HIT RECORD TOMORROW. I NEED A GUITARIST – THE JOB'S YOURS IF YOU WANT IT.

THANKS VERY MUCH.

But old Mrs Morris wasn't celebrating...

TONY WHITE – I FIRED YOU. GET OUT OF HERE!

YOU MUST BE MRS MORRIS. I'LL BUY YOUR CAFE.

HERE'S £15,000. DON'T COME BACK.

AND I WANT YOU TO RUN THE CAFE FOR ME, CINDY.

YOU'RE IN CHARGE FROM NOW ON.

OH THANKYOU MR GEORGE.

A few weeks later and the cafe is full once more. The customers had flooded back to hear the sensational sounds of Tony's guitar.

I SAY! ISN'T THAT TONY WHITE, THE NEW POP STAR?

YES IT IS, AND I'M THE NEW MRS WHITE!

THE END

Photography by Colin Davison. Restaurant supplied by WILLOW TEAS, Jesmond. Billy George's footwear by Mitch.

A Viz Comic Production © 1984

OKAY JOE. ALL SET TO TEST MY NEW IMPACT RESISTANT CRASH HELMET?

YEP!

BOOM!

ANOTHER PARTIAL SUCCESS

FELIX AND HIS AMAZING UNDERPANTS

CD 10.84

IF YOU HELP ME TO PICK MY APPLES, YOU CAN KEEP AS MANY AS YOU CAN CARRY

OKAY, VICAR

AN HOUR LATER...

THANKS VICAR! SEE YOU LATER

UH?!?

PHEW! WHAT A FEAST... OH NO! HERE COMES BASHER BILL. WHERE CAN I HIDE?

FUNNY! I'M SURE I SAW THAT FELIX AROUND HERE SOMEWHERE

SHORTLY...

HMM! I'VE STILL GOT ONE APPLE LEFT...

I WONDER HOW FAR I CAN FIRE IT USING MY UNDERPANTS AS A CATAPULT

PRANG!!

AGH!

OH CRIKEY! I'VE KNOCKED P.C. PORTER OFF HIS BICYCLE!!

CRUMBS! MY BICYCLE IS RUINED

YOU'LL JUST HAVE TO CARRY ME ROUND IN YOUR UNDERPANTS UNTIL I CAN GET IT MENDED, EH FELIX?

Mr. LOGIC

SUCH IS MY NAME, THEREFORE IT WOULD ONLY BE CORRECT TO MAKE AN ASUMPTION THAT THIS COMIC STRIP IS IN SOME WAY ABOUT ME.

HE'S A PAIN IN THE ARSE!

hmm... A MARKET, A GATHERING FOR SALE OF COMMODITIES OR LIVESTOCK.

FRUIT   **CLOTHES**

COME ALONG NOW FOLKS, GET YOUR APPLES AND ORANGES!

WHITE SPORTS SOCKS... THREE PAIRS FOR A POUND!

hmm... THE MAN ON THE RIGHT RUNS A CLOTHING STALL, YET HE APPEARS TO BE SELLING PEARS, A FLESHY FRUIT WHICH TAPERS TOWARD THE STALK, SURELY THIS MUST BE SOME KIND OF MISDEMEANOUR, I SHALL MAKE RELEVANT INQUIRIES...

YOU RUN A CLOTHING STALL DO YOU NOT?

YEAH! SO WHAT?

YOU ARE OFFERING THE SALE OF PEARS AT A PRICE OF THREE FOR A POUND, SURELY THIS IS NOT IN KEEPING WITH YOUR BUSINESS

EH?!

FRUIT IS NOT A COMMON FORM OF WEARING-APPAREL

WHAT?!

PEOPLE DO NOT WEAR FRUIT AS CLOTHING, IS IT NOT THEREFORE AN INDESCREPANCY TO SELL IT AS SUCH?

YOU'RE BLOODY CRAZY!

CRAZY? oh yes...UNSOUND, SHAKY, HALF-WITTED, MAD, OR, IN THE CASE OF PAVING FOR INSTANCE, IRREGULAR PIECES FITTED TOGETHER. I FIND YOUR STATEMENT PUZZLING.

ARE YOU BUYING ANYTHING YOUNG MAN? I WOULD LIKE TO GET SOME SOCKS!

AT PRESENT I AM IN THE PROCESS OF ESTABLISHING THE NATURE OF THIS PERSON'S BUSINESS, BUT I HAVE BEEN SIDE-TRACKED INTO A DISCUSSION ABOUT MENTAL HEALTH.

DON'T BOTHER, I THINK HE'S A CRACKER!

GRRR!

CRACKER-FIREWORK, PAPER CYLINDER CONTAINING SMALL TOY ETC. AND EXPLODING WHEN ENDS ARE PULLED, THIN, CRISP BISCUIT... **END**

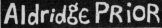

No. 9   November 1982

No. 10   May 1983

No. 11   May 1984

No. 12   November 1984

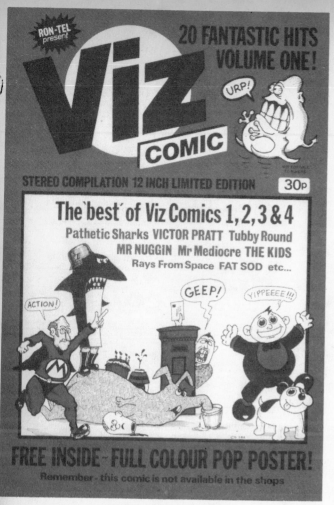

No. 10½ November 1983

No. 12a May 1985

New 'High Fibre' Viz Comic is now published more REGULARLY than ever before.

For subscription details send a SAE to:

BIG HARD ENQUIRIES DEPT.

Viz Comic Subscriptions
328 Kensal Road
London
W10 5XJ

For details of recent back issues send another SAE to:

DEPT. BIG HARD / BACK ISSUES

Viz House
16 Lily Crescent
Newcastle upon Tyne
NE2 2SP